When grief is

When grief is raw

SONGS FOR TIMES OF SORROW AND BEREAVEMENT

John L. Bell
and
Graham Maule

WILD GOOSE PUBLICATIONS
Iona Community
GLASGOW

First published 1997

ISBN 0 947988 91 2

Published by Wild Goose Publications

Wild Goose Publications, Unit 15, Six Harmony Row, Glasgow G51 3BA

Wild Goose Publications is the publishing division of the Iona Community.
Scottish Charity No. SC003794. Limited Company Reg. No SCO96243.

The Wild Goose is the Celtic symbol of the Holy Spirit.
It is the trademark of Wild Goose Publications.

Distributed in Australia and New Zealand by Willow Connection Pty Ltd,
Unit 7A, 3-9 Kenneth Road, Manly Vale NSW 2093.

Permission to reproduce any part of this work in Australia or New Zealand
should be sought from Willow Connection.

A catalogue record for this book is available from the British Library.

Printed by The Cromwell Press Ltd, Melksham, Wilts.

Contents

Introduction

Three main factors lie behind this collection of songs.

The first is the comment made some years ago by a ministerial colleague who noted that there was a dearth of material suitable to be sung at funerals and memorial services.

As often as not, the undertaker suggests that the family choose their or the deceased's favourite hymn, and inevitably either 'Psalm 23' or 'Abide With Me' appear on the service sheet. Recent years have seen the addition of 'Thine Be the Glory' as an alternative to the former two or as a counter-attraction to 'The Old Rugged Cross'.

Unlike the sacraments of Baptism and Holy Communion, ceremonies surrounding death are offered by the churches to everyone, yet minimal attention has been paid to what is both accessible and representative in respect of texts and tunes for those who mourn.

The second contributory factor was our discovery of the immense range of emotion in the Psalms. When we were working on *Psalms of Patience, Protest and Praise,* we were recurrently startled by the daring honesty with which the writers could complain to, as well as praise, their Creator.

It may be that limp musical settings of these ancient texts or presumed over-familiarity with them has dulled our senses to the direct, raw pleading and complaining which is as necessary for a healthy faith as adoration.

In the wake of the tragedy at Dunblane Primary School in March 1996, a colleague said with evident dismay, 'It's now I realize that we've forgotten how to lament.' Perhaps the antidote to this feeling of inadequacy is to familiarize ourselves with the scriptural songs which Jesus knew by rote, and which for all time can offer the depth of human sorrow to the heart of God.

Thirdly, these—as all our songs—could never have been written were it not for our interaction with the people of God and with the Word of God. No material here was ever written 'for publication.' This book is the consequence of songs resonating in situations other than that for which they were first intended, rather than the goal behind our writing.

8

We believe that essentially a hymn should convey what God has to say to the people and/or what the people need to say to God. We are therefore keen to record our gratitude to those who have discussed the scriptures with us and shared those sorrows which informed our words.

The recording of THE LAST JOURNEY collection by The Cathedral Singers of Chicago afforded the opportunity to allow words and music for times of grieving to be presented in a choral medium. But there still remained the challenge to provide texts and tunes for all God's people. In response to that challenge, this book is offered.

The vast majority of the songs here have been arranged for congregational use. It is anticipated that they will be sung either *a cappella* or accompanied on keyboard or, occasionally, guitar. While several of the tunes may be new, most of the songs are in metres which allow for alternative melodies to be adopted.

However, that should not inhibit the occasional introduction of a new tune even at a requiem mass or funeral service. The authors of these texts well remember one such occasion when, because of the desire of a grieving congregation to articulate its sorrow, the hymn which was barely audible in verse 1, was sung with intensity by verse 5.

Nevertheless, there are occasions on which the depth of anguish which a people share makes their common voice weak. Then, an unobtrusive and sensitive individual may sing the words solo, while others follow the text. Or, if there is a choir in the church, the octavo arrangements of many of these texts may be worth putting into the vocabulary of the singers. A choir which functions well in a funeral situation is not one which has just 'got up' an appropriate anthem. It is one where the conductor has the foresight to prepare the singers for all eventualities.

It is our hope that these songs may enable God's people to speak honestly to their Maker when grief is raw, just as other songs enable their praise to be represented when joy is deep.

John L. Bell
Graham Maule
Lent 1997

SONGS
FOR
THE TIME OF GRIEVING

10 Who is there to understand?

CARRINGTON (JLB)

faltering, as the text demands ♩ = 60

1. All the fears I need to name but am too scared to say;
2. All the wast - ed years in which I strug - gled to be free;
3. What the cause of pain is and, much more, the rea - son why;
4. 'All the wrong you now ad - mit, I prom - ise to for - give;

all the shame for what I've done which noth - ing can al - lay;
all the bro - ken prom - is - es that took their toll on me;
what my fi - nal hour will bring, how sud - den - ly I'll die;
all that you re - gret, you are not sen - tenced to re - live;

all the peo - ple I've let down and lost a - long the way;
all the love I should have shown and all I failed to be;
what the fu - ture holds for those I'll miss, for whom I cry;
all the love you've nev - er known is mine a - lone to give;

all the hate I still re - mand: must
all I longed to take my hand: must
what, too late, I might de - mand: shall
you, my child are un - der - stood. So

12

these   tor - ment me to the end   of time?
these   tor - ment me to the end   of time?
these   tor - ment me to the end   of time?
do   not fear all that is yet   to be:

Who is there to un - der - stand?
Who is there to un - der - stand?
Who is there to un - der - stand?
heaven is close and God is good.'

*last verse
only*

1. All the fears I need to name but am too scared to say;
   all the shame for what I've done which nothing can allay;
   all the people I've let down and lost along the way;
   all the hate I still remand:
   must these torment me to the end of time?
   Who is there to understand?

2. All the wasted years in which I struggled to be free;
   all the broken promises that took their toll on me;
   all the love I should have shown and all I failed to be;
   all I longed to take my hand:
   must these torment me to the end of time?
   Who is there to understand?

3. What the cause of pain is and, much more, the reason why;
   what my final hour will bring, how suddenly I'll die;
   what the future holds for those I'll miss, for whom I cry;
   what, too late, I might demand:
   shall these torment me to the end of time?
   Who is there to understand?

4. 'All the wrong you now admit, I promise to forgive;
   all that you regret, you are not sentenced to relive;
   all the love you've never known is mine alone to give;
   you, my child are understood.
   So do not fear all that is yet to be:
   heaven is close and God is good.'

For many people, grief is such a sudden and isolating experience that they feel no-one can appreciate what they are going through. This song, based on the conversation of one such person moves from a statement of the human confusion to an intimation of God's response.

It should be sung solo, though a different voice would be appropriate for the final verse.

This song is featured in the CD/Cassette and Octavo collection entitled THE LAST JOURNEY. The individual octavo arrangement for keyboard, voice and cello may be found in the GIA catalogue No.: G4528

14

How long, O Lord?

NEW THIRTEENTH (JLB)
Text: Psalm 13 (para. JLB)

slow and bluesy ♩ = 54

1. How long, O Lord, will you quite for-get
2. How long, O Lord, must this grief pos-sess my
3. Look now, look now and an - swer me, my

me? How long, O Lord, will you
heart? How long, O Lord, must I
God; give light, give light lest I

15

turn   your face from   me?   How   long,   O
lan - guish night and   day?   How   long,   O
sleep   the   sleep of   death.   Lest my en - e -

Lord,   must I   suf-fer   in   my   soul?   How
Lord,   shall my en - e -   my   op - press?   How
mies   re - joice at   my   down - fall,   look

16

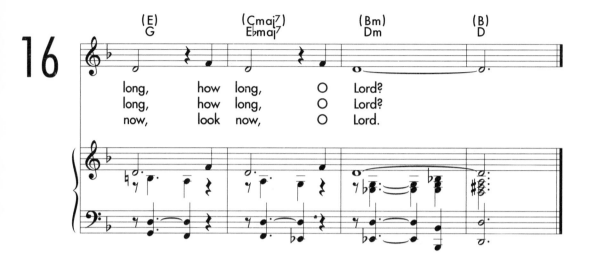

long,   how long,   O Lord?
long,   how long,   O Lord?
now,   look now,   O Lord.

1. How long, O Lord, will you quite forget me?
   How long, O Lord, will you turn your face from me?
   How long, O Lord, must I suffer in my soul?
   How long, how long, O Lord?

2. How long, O Lord, must this grief possess my heart?
   How long, O Lord, must I languish night and day?
   How long, O Lord, shall my enemy oppress?
   How long, how long, O Lord?

3. Look now, look now and answer me, my God;
   give light, give light lest I sleep the sleep of death.
   Lest my enemies rejoice at my downfall,
   look now, look now, O Lord.

However down and unhappy people feel, someone in the Bible will have been there before them. It is an immense source of consolation that all through the centuries Jews and Christians have sung their despair to God, using the words of the psalms.

When such poems are used, we stand in solidarity with a great host of believers, including Jesus, who found consolation in knowing that God could take all their questions and despair. This is another solo lament, though the congregation may be encouraged to join the final verse.

This song is featured in the CD/Cassette and Octavo Collections entitled THE LAST JOURNEY. The individual octavo arrangement for voice, keyboard and cello may be found in the GIA catalogue No. G-4531

18 We cannot measure how you heal

YE BANKS AND BRAES Scots trad. (arr. JLB)

gently ♩ = 90

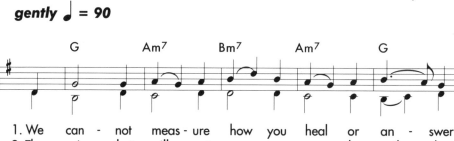

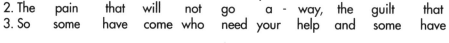

1. We can - not meas - ure how you heal or an - swer
2. The pain that will not go a - way, the guilt that
3. So some have come who need your help and some have

eve - ry suffe - rer's prayer, yet we be -
clings from things long past, the fear of
come to make a - mends, as hands which

19

20

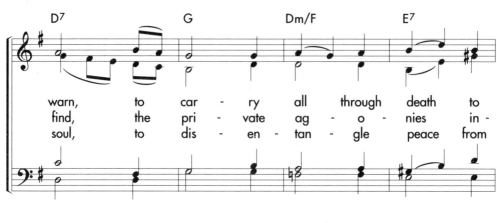

warn, to car - ry all through death to
find, the pri - vate ag - o - nies in -
soul, to dis - en - tan - gle peace from

life and cra - dle chil - dren yet un - born.
side, the mem - o - ries that haunt the mind.
pain and make your bro - ken peo - ple whole.

1. We cannot measure how you heal
   or answer everry sufferer's prayer,
   yet we believe your grace responds
   where faith and doubt unite to care.
   Your hands, though bloodied on the cross,
   survive to hold and heal and warn,
   to carry all through death to life
   and cradle children yet unborn.

2. The pain that will not go away,
   the guilt that clings from things long past,
   the fear of what the future holds,
   are present as if meant to last.
   But present too is love which tends
   the hurt we never hoped to find,
   the private agonies inside,
   the memories that haunt the mind.

3. So some have come who need your help
   and some have come to make amends,
   as hands which shaped and saved the world
   are present in the touch of friends.
   Lord, let your Spirit meet us here
   to mend the body, mind and soul,
   to disentangle peace from pain
   and make your broken people whole.

Though originally written for use at service of healing, this song has been used to good effect in situations of loss and at requiem masses or funeral services. The tune, one of the most universally known Scottish traditional melodies, makes for effortless singing.

22 I cry to God

Tune: NEW 77TH (JLB)
Text: Psalm 77 (para. JLB)

lamentoso ♩ = 48

1. I cry to God and he hears me; in my
2. I think of God and I moan; I
3. I thought of days gone by, and re-
4. Will God re-ject us for-ev-er? Will
5. Has God for-got-ten to be gra-cious? Has
(6.) me now re-mem-ber God's work and re-

times of trou-ble I seek him. By
med-i-tate and feel use-less. God
mem-bered times now van-ished. I
God re-fuse us his mer-cy? Has
an-ger doused his com-pass-ion? Has God's
call his won-der-ful great-ness. Let me

night   my hands plead in prayer,   but I
keeps   the sleep from my eyes,   and my
spent   the night in deep dis - tress   while my
end - less love reached an end?   Are God's
might - y arm lost its grasp?   Does it
med - i - tate on his power   and re -

find   noth - ing for my com - fort.
speech   is lost   in con - fu - sion.
spir - it mur - mured with - in me.
prom - i - ses   now in - val - id?
hang   pow - er - less be - side him?   6. Let
mem - ber all   God has done.

24

1. I cry to God and he hears me;
   in my times of trouble I seek him.
   By night my hands plead in prayer,
   but I find nothing for my comfort.

2. I think of God and I moan;
   I meditate and feel useless.
   God keeps the sleep from my eyes,
   and my speech is lost in confusion.

3. I thought of days gone by,
   and remembered times now vanished.
   I spent the night in deep distress
   while my spirit murmured within me.

4. Will God reject us forever?
   Will God refuse us his mercy?
   Has endless love reached an end?
   Are God's promises now invalid?

5. Has God forgotten to be gracious?
   Has anger doused his compassion?
   Has God's mighty arm lost its grasp?
   Does it hang powerless beside him?

6. Let me now remember God's work
   and recall his wonderful greatness.
   Let me meditate on his power
   and remember all God has done.

This psalm is representative of the mood swings which people experience in times of grief. We believe...and yet we doubt; and we sense sometimes the absence of the God we want to affirm. Again, the consolation of Scripture is that such a reaction is nothing if not normal.

This song is featured in the CD/Cassette and Octavo collections entitled THE LAST JOURNEY. The individual Octavo arrangement for choir, organ, oboe and flute may be found in the GIA Catalogue No.: G4530

26 Word of the Father

Tune: WORD OF THE FATHER (JLB)

gently ♩ = 90

1. Word of the Father,
   come, Lord, come;
   and take our fear away,
   and take our fear away;
   replace it with your love.

2. Firstborn of Mary,...

3. Healer and helper,...

4. Servant and sufferer,...

5. Jesus, redeemer,...

6. Christ resurrected,...

7. Maranatha!...

This simple call and response song may be sung *a cappella* in harmony or with a cantor and congregation accompanied by keyboard. It may be useful as a prelude to worship, an entrance song or a communion hymn.

SONGS
OF
CONSOLATION

30

A woman's care

Tune: DIED FOR LOVE English trad. (arr. JLB)
Text: Isaiah Ch. 49 (para JLB)

gently ♩. = 48

1. When trou - ble strikes and fear takes root, and
2. Our wan - dering minds be - lieve the worst and
3. God says, 'See how a wo - man cares. Can
4. 'My dear - est daugh - ter, fond - est son, my
5. Then praise the Lord through faith and fear, in

dreams are dry and sense un - sound; when
ask, as faith and fer - vour fade, 'Has
she for - get the child she bore? Even
wea - ry folk in eve - ry land, your
ho - ly and in hope - less place; for

31

hope   be - comes   a   bar - ren   waste,   then
God   now   turned   his   back   on   us   for -
if   she   did,   I   shan't   for - get: though
souls   are   cra - dled   in   my   heart,   your
height   and   depth   and   heaven   and   hell   can't

doubts   like   moun - tains   soar   a - round.
sak - ing   those   he   loved   and   made?'
feel - ing   lost,   I   love   you   more.'
names   are   writ - ten   on   my   hand.'
keep   us   far   from   God's   em - brace.

32

1. When trouble strikes and fear takes root,
   and dreams are dry and sense unsound;
   when hope becomes a barren waste,
   the doubts like mountains soar around.

2. Our wandering minds believe the worst
   and ask, as faith and fervour fade,
   'Has God now turned his back on us
   forsaking those he loved and made?'

3. God says, 'See how a woman cares.
   Can she forget the child she bore?
   Even if she did, I shan't forget:
   though feeling lost, I love you more.'

4. 'My dearest daughter, fondest son,
   my weary folk in every land,
   your souls are cradled in my heart,
   your names are written on my hand.'

5. Then praise the Lord through faith and fear,
   in holy and in hopeless place;
   for height and depth and heaven and hell
   can't keep us far from God's embrace.

From childhood, it is often our mother to whom we run in times of distress. There is something in the understanding of the mother which we feel we can trust. How appropriate, therefore, that God, in several passages of Isaiah's prophecy, should speak of the divine self in terms of a woman, a mid-wife and a mother.

If this is being sung by a congregation, the women should sing verses 3 & 4 on their own.

An alternative tune in Long Metre is ROCKINGHAM.

34 God was there

ROBERTSON (JLB)

moderato ♩ = 54

1. When the wind on cha - os blew,
2. Where the ear - liest mor - tals talked,
3. While the trades - man was de - cried,
4. God was there but not in vain.
5. In each dark - ness, cloud and fire,
6. Not for what we are or do,

when the world from noth - ing grew,
where the vir - gin land was walked,
while the sav - iour was de - nied,
Shield - ing joy and shar - ing pain,
in the quiet as words re - tire,
not for what we've jour - neyed through,

when   the pri - mal   dream   came   true,
where   e - mer - gent   faith   was   rocked,
while   his son was   cru   -   ci - fied,
rais   -   ing life to   live   a - gain,
in   our loss and   best   de - sire,
but   for all you   call   us   to,

God   was   there.
God   was   there.
God   was   there.
God   was   there.
God   is   there.
God,   be   there.

36

1. When the wind on chaos blew,
   when the world from nothing grew,
   when the primal dream came true,
   God was there.

2. Where the earliest mortals talked,
   where the virgin land was walked,
   where emergent faith was rocked,
   God was there.

3. While the tradesman was decried,
   while the saviour was denied,
   while his son was crucified,
   God was there.

4. God was there but not in vain.
   Shielding joy and sharing pain,
   raising life to live again,
   God was there.

5. In each darkness, cloud and fire,
   in the quiet as words retire,
   in our loss and best desire,
   God is there.

6. Not for what we are or do,
   not for what we've journeyed through,
   but for all you call us to,
   God, be there.

If one were to write a history of God, it would be one in which God's love does not provide a safe cocoon, but rather demands risk and vulnerability. The Bible repeatedly offers us insights into the heart of God which hurts, yearns and weeps until, in Jesus, God takes flesh and lives in solidarity with us that we might know that nothing can separate us from his love.

Let your restless hearts be still 37

Tune: *THE LARK IN THE CLEAR AIR* Irish trad. (arr. JLB)
Text: *John 14 (para. JLB)*

very gently ♩ = 60

1. Let your rest - less hearts be still, let your
2. Where I am and where I'll be, is where

troub - led minds be rest - ed; trust in God to lift your
you shall live for - ev - er; and the way to where I

Words & Arrangement: © 1988, 1996 WGRG, The Iona Community, Glasgow G51 3UU Scotland

38

care   and, in   car - ing,   trust   in   me.   In   God's
go   I   have   walked   a - mong   you   here.   I'm   the

house   you   have   a   place —   were   it   oth - er - wise   I
Way   that   nev - er   ends,   I'm   the   Truth   that

would   have   told   you.   This   I   glad - ly   go   to   pre -
nev - er   chang - es,   I'm   the   Life   that   nev - er

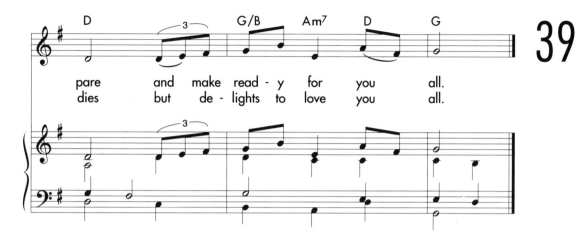

pare and make read - y for you all.
dies but de - lights to love you all.

1. Let your restless hearts be still,
   let your troubled minds be rested;
   trust in God to lift your care
   and in caring, trust in me.
   In God's house you have a place —
   were it otherwise I would have told you.
   This I gladly go to prepare
   and make ready for you all.

2. Where I am and where I'll be,
   is where you shall live forever;
   and the way to where I go
   I have walked among you here.
   I'm the Way that never ends,
   I'm the Truth that never changes
   I'm the Life that never dies
   but delights to love you all.

This is a solo song which may be sung during a funeral service or on some other occasion when the assurance of Christ's peace is of utmost importance.

This song is featured in the CD/Cassette and Octavo collections entitled THE LAST JOURNEY. The individual octavo arrangement for soloist and choir may be found in the GIA catalogue No: G4532.

40

Sing, my soul

Tune: MYSIE (JLB)

gently ♩ = 72

1. Sing, my soul, when hope is sleep - ing, sing when
2. Sing, my soul, when sick - ness lin - gers, sing to
3. Sing, my soul, of him who shaped me, let me
4. Sing, my soul, when light seems dark - est, sing when

faith gives way to fears; sing to melt the ice of
dull the sharp - est pain; sing to set the spir - it
wan - der far a - way, ran with o - pen arms to
night re - fus - es rest, sing though death should mock the

sad - ness, mak - ing way for joy through tears.
leap - ing: heal - ing needs a glad re - frain.
greet me, brought me home a - gain to stay.
fu - ture: what's to come by God is blessed.

1. Sing, my soul, when hope is sleeping,
   sing when faith gives way to fears;
   sing to melt the ice of sadness,
   making way for joy through tears.

2. Sing, my soul, when sickness lingers,
   sing to dull the sharpest pain;
   sing to set the spirit leaping:
   healing needs a glad refrain.

3. Sing, my soul, of him who shaped me,
   let me wander far away,
   ran with open arms to greet me,
   brought me home again to stay.

4. Sing, my soul, when light seems darkest,
   sing when night refuses rest,
   sing though death should mock the future:
   what's to come by God is blessed.

This essentially solo song is a paraphrase of a letter from an elderly saintly woman whose testimony is that, even in her lowest days, when she speaks to God, he listens. Then she sings to rejoice both her heart and his. It is well suited to the Saturday of Holy Week or to other occasions when loss or weakness is evident.

42

Be still

Tune: BE STILL (JLB)
Text: Psalm 46, verse 10

quietly but steadily ♩ = 54

Be still and know that I am God. Be still and

God Be still and know that I am God.

D.C. last time only

know that I am God.

Be still and know that I am God.

Be still and know that I am God.
Be still and know that I am God.

This simple chant can be sung solo or in canon with another voice, or the congregation may be invited to join in the singing.

This song is featured in the CD/Cassette and Octavo Collections entitled GOD NEVER SLEEPS. The individual octavo arrangement for two soloists and choir may be found in the GIA catalogue No.: G-4382

SONGS
FOR
GOD'S HELP

46 Since we are summoned

Tune: SILENT PLACE (JLB)

very gently ♩ = 52

1. Since we are sum-moned to a si-lent place, strug-gling to find some words to
2. Since we are sav-aged by the pain of loss, stopped at a bar-rier we have
3. Since we are forced to face this last fare-well, sad-dened to depths we nev-er
4. Christ be be-neath us, Christ be all a-bove, Christ take the hand of *her* we've

fill the space; Christ be be-side us as we
yet to cross; Christ be be-side us as we
could fore - tell; Christ be be-side us as we
lost and love; take her to par - a - dise and

grieve, dar - ing to doubt or to be - lieve.
mourn, bro - ken, dis - con - so - late and torn.
weep, loos - 'ning our hold on whom you'll keep.
then Christ be be-side us once a - gain.

48

1. Since we are summoned to a silent place,
   struggling to find some words to fill the space;
   Christ be beside us as we grieve,
   daring to doubt or to believe.

2. Since we are savaged by the pain of loss,
   stopped at a barrier we have yet to cross;
   Christ be beside us as we mourn,
   broken, disconsolate and torn.

3. Since we are forced to face this last farewell,
   saddened to depths we never could foretell;
   Christ be beside us as we weep,
   loosening our hold on whom you'll keep.

4. Christ be beneath us, Christ be all above,
   Christ take the hand of *her* we've lost and love;
   Take *her* to paradise and then
   Christ be beside us once again.

For some people, the Silent Place may be the church or the funeral parlour, or the room in their home where they have to come to terms with unwanted loss. Drawing on the words of people who have been in that place, this song articulates their deep longings.

This song is featured in the CD/Cassette and Octavo collections entitled THE LAST JOURNEY. The individual octavo arrangement for choir, keyboard and cello may be found in the GIA catalogue No.: G4536.

50

O Christ, you wept

Tune: PALMER (JLB)

gently ♩ = 60

1. O Christ, you wept when grief was raw, and
2. The well - loved voice is si - lent now and
3. We try to hold what is not here and
4. In all our lone - li - ness and doubt, through

felt for those who mourned their friend; come
we have much we meant to say; col -
fear for what we do not know; oh,
what we can - not re - al - ize, ad -

51

52

1. O Christ, you wept when grief was raw,
   and felt for those who mourned their friend;
   come close to where we would not be
   and hold us, numbed by this life's end.

2. The well-loved voice is silent now
   and we have much we meant to say;
   collect our lost and wandering words
   and keep them till the endless day.

3. We try to hold what is not here
   and fear for what we do not know;
   oh, take our hands in yours, good Lord,
   and free us to let our friend go.

4. In all our loneliness and doubt
   through what we cannot realize,
   address us from your empty tomb
   and tell us that life never dies.

The shortest verse in the Bible, 'Jesus wept' appears in the 11th chapter of John's gospel where the sorrow of the sisters and friends of Lazarus brings Jesus himself to tears. If anyone ever wondered whether Christ really had a human heart, this story is ample proof.

This song is featured in the CD/Cassette and Octavo Collections entitled THE LAST JOURNEY. The individual octavo arrangement for choir, keyboard and flute may be found in the GIA catalogue No.: G-4529

54 God give us life

Tune: CAMPBELL (JLB)

quietly but firmly ♩ = 65

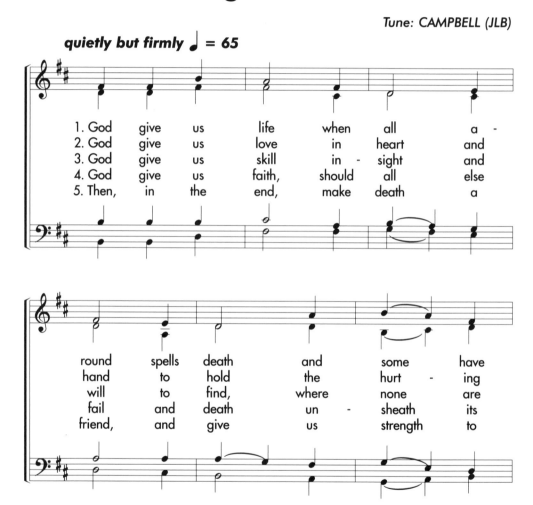

1. God give us life when all a-round spells death and some have
2. God give us love in heart and hand to hold the hurt-ing
3. God give us skill in - sight and will to find, where none are
4. God give us faith, should all else fail and death un - sheath its
5. Then, in the end, make death a friend, and give us strength to

died;   and   none   are   clear   that   hope   is
one,   to   free   the   an - ger,   meet   the
sure,   new   threads   to   mend   the   web   of
sting.   O   help   us   hear,   through   pain   and
stand   and   walk   to   where   no   eye   can

near   or   fate   can   be   de - fied.
need   and   wait   till   wait - ing's   done.
life,   new   means   to   heal   and   cure.
fear,   the   songs   that   an - gels   sing.
stare,   but   Christ   can   clasp   our   hand.

56

1. God give us life
   when all around spells death,
   and some have died;
   and none are clear that hope is near
   or fate can be defied.

2. God give us love
   in heart and hand
   to hold the hurting one,
   to free the anger, meet the need
   and wait till waiting's done.

3. God give us skill,
   insight and will
   to find, where none are sure,
   new threads to mend the web of life,
   new means to heal and cure.

4. God give us faith,
   should all else fail
   and death unsheath its sting.
   O help us hear, through pain and fear,
   the songs that angels sing.

5. Then, in the end,
   make death a friend,
   and give us strength to stand
   and walk to where no eye can stare,
   but Christ can clasp our hand.

When one of our friends was dying from cancer, it became evident that there were more people to pray for than the patient. Those who visited, those who cared professionally, those who were involved in medical research—all these and more are involved in the drama of life beginning and ending and beginning again.

Each verse of this song, therefore, allows for different people to be prayed for.

58 A touching place

Tune: DREAM ANGUS Scots trad. (arr. JLB)

tenderly ♩. = 48

1. Christ's is the world in which we move,
2. Feel for the peo - ple we most a - void,
3. Feel for the par - ents who've lost their child,
4. Feel for the lives by life con - fused,

Christ's are the folk we're sum - moned to love,
strange or be - reaved or nev - er em - ployed;
feel for the wom - en whom men have de - filed,
rid - dled with doubt, in lov - ing a - bused;

59

Christ's is the voice which calls us to care, and
feel for the wom-en and feel for the men who
feel for the ba-by for whom there's no breast, and
feel for the lone-ly heart, con-scious of sin, which

Christ is the one who meets us here.
fear that their liv-ing is all in vain.
feel for the wea-ry who find no rest.
longs to be pure but fears to be-gin.

TO THE LOST, CHRIST SHOWS HIS FACE;

60

TO THE UN - LOVED, HE GIVES HIS EM - BRACE;

TO THOSE WHO CRY IN PAIN OR DIS - GRACE, CHRIST

MAKES, WITH HIS FRIENDS, A TOUCH - ING PLACE.

1. Christ's is the world in which we move,
   Christ's are the folk we're summoned to love,
   Christ's is the voice which calls us to care,
   and Christ is the one who meets us here.

Chorus: *TO THE LOST, CHRIST SHOWS HIS FACE;*
                    TO THE UNLOVED, HE GIVES HIS EMBRACE;
                    TO THOSE WHO CRY IN PAIN OR DISGRACE,
                    CHRIST MAKES, WITH HIS FRIENDS,
                    A TOUCHING PLACE.

2. Feel for the people we most avoid,
   strange or bereaved or never employed;
   feel for the women and feel for the men
   who fear that their living is all in vain.

3. Feel for the parents who've lost their child,
   feel for the women whom men have defiled,
   feel for the baby for whom there's no breast,
   and feel for the weary who find no rest.

4. Feel for the lives by life confused,
   riddled with doubt, in loving abused;
   feel for the lonely heart, conscious of sin,
   which longs to be pure but fears to begin.

This, which is one of our earliest songs, was written to enable the healing service in Iona Abbey. The words draw on the great Celtic theme of the Incarnate Christ who did and always will touch his people, and the tune is that of a Gaelic lullaby…a woman's working song.

This song is featured in the CD/Cassette and Octavo Collections entitled GOD NEVER SLEEPS. The individual octavo arrangement for soloist and choir may be found in the GIA catalogue No.: G4377

62 Calm in the storm

Tune: CALM IN THE STORM (JLB)

steadily ♩= 48

1. Calm in the storm, foot-path and friend in the dark,
2. Where faith is low, where hope has noth-ing to show,
3. Lives bruised and torn, ba-bies a - bout to be born,
4. Calm in the storm, foot-path and friend in the dark,

song in the night; trust-ing your touch in - to your
where love is spent; there show your face, there let your
folk near - ing death — send each an an - gel or a
song in the night; glo - ry to you, Sav-iour and

care we com - mit those hid from sight.
heav - en - ly grace fond - ly be sent.
word or a sign, warm with your breath.
Lord, strength and shield, lift - er and light.

1. Calm in the storm,
   footpath and friend in the dark,
   song in the night;
   trusting your touch
   into your care we commit
   those hid from sight.

2. Where faith is low,
   where hope has nothing to show,
   where love is spent;
   there show your face,
   there let your heavenly grace
   fondly be sent.

3. Lives bruised and torn,
   babies about to be born,
   folk nearing death —
   send each an angel
   or a word or a sign,
   warm with your breath.

4. Calm in the storm,
   footpath and friend in the dark,
   song in the night;
   glory to you, Saviour and Lord,
   strength and shield,
   lifter and light.

The promise of Christian faith is not that those who believe will have an easy life, but that in every difficulty they face, God will not abandon them. Hence, Jesus does not avoid the storm, but accompanies his disciples through it.

SONGS
OF
LEAVE TAKING

66

The last journey

IONA BOAT SONG Scots trad. (arr. JLB)

1. From the fal - ter of breath, through the
2. From frus - tra - tion and pain, through hope
3. From the dim - ming of light, through the
4. From to - day till we die, through all

si - lence of death, to the won - der that's
hard to sus - tain, to the whole - ness here
dark - ness of night, to the glo - ry of
ques - tion - ing why, to the place from which

67

break - ing be - yond;
prom - ised, there known;
good - ness a - bove;
time and tide flow;

God has wo - ven a
Christ has gone where we
God the Spir - it is
an - gels tread on our

way, un - ap - par - ent by day, for all
fear and has vowed to be near on the
sent to en - sure heaven's in - tent is em -
dreams, and mag - ni - fi - cent themes of heaven's

those of whom heav - en is fond.
jour - ney we make on our own.
braced and com - plet - ed in love.
prom - ise are ech - oed be - low.

68

1. From the falter of breath,
   through the silence of death,
   to the wonder that's breaking beyond;
   God has woven a way,
   unapparent by day,
   for all those of whom heaven is fond.

2. From frustration and pain,
   through hope hard to sustain,
   to the wholeness here promised, there known;
   Christ has gone where we fear
   and has vowed to be near
   on the journey we make our own.

3. From the dimming of light,
   through the darkness of night,
   to the glory of goodness above;
   God the Spirit is sent
   to ensure heaven's intent
   is embraced and completed in love.

4. From today till we die,
   through all questioning why,
   to the place from which time and tide flow;
   angels tread on our dreams,
   and magnificent themes
   of heaven's promise are echoed below.

Legend has it that this tune was used as ancient Scottish kings were, after death, rowed to their resting place on the island of Iona. It would be a pity if such a fine tune were reserved solely for the use of royalty.

This song is featured in the CD/Cassette and Octavo Collections entitled THE LAST JOURNEY. The individual octavo arrangement for choir, flute and cello may be found in the GIA catalogue. No.: G4535

Go, silent friend

Tune: Psalm12 LONDONDERRY AIR (arr. JLB)

warmly ♩ = 45

1. Go, si - lent friend, your life has found its end - ing;
2. Go, si - lent friend, for - give us if we grieved you;

to dust re - turns your wea - ry mor - tal frame.
safe now in heav - en, kind - ly say our name.

69

70

God, who be-fore   birth called you in-to   be - ing,
Your life has touched   us,   that   is   why we   mourn   you;

now calls you   hence,   his   ac-cent still the   same.
our lives with - out   you   can-not be the   same.

Go, si-lent   friend,   your   life   in Christ   is   bur - ied;
Go, si-lent   friend,   we   do   not grudge you   glo - ry;

for you he lived and died and rose a - gain. Close by his
sing, sing with joy deep prais- es to your Lord. You, who be-

side your prom - ised place is wait - ing where, ful - ly
lieved that Christ would come back for you, now cel - e -

1.
known, you shall with God re - main.
brate that Je - sus keeps his

2.
word.

72

Go, silent friend

Tune: Psalm 12 DONNE SECOURS (arr. JLB)

firmly ♩ = 80

1. Go, si - lent friend, your life has found its end - ing;
2. Go, si - lent friend, your life in Christ is bur - ied;
3. Go, si - lent friend, for - give us if we grieved you;
4. Go, si - lent friend, we do not grudge you glo - ry;

to dust re - turns your wea - ry mor - tal frame.
for you he lived and died and rose a - gain.
safe now in heav - en, kind - ly say our name.
sing, sing with joy deep prais - es to your Lord.

God, who be - fore birth called you in - to be - ing,
Close by his side your prom - ised place is wait - ing
Your life has touched us, that is why we mourn you;
You, who be - lieved that Christ would come back for you,

now calls you hence, his ac - cent still the same.
where, ful - ly known, you shall with God re - main.
our lives with - out you can - not be the same.
now cel - e - brate that Je - sus keeps his word.

1. Go, silent friend,
   your life has found its ending;
   to dust returns
   your weary mortal frame.
   God, who before birth
   called you into being,
   now calls you hence,
   his accent still the same.

2. Go, silent friend,
   your life in Christ is buried;
   for you he lived
   and died and rose again.
   Close by his side
   your promised place is waiting
   where, fully known,
   you shall with God remain.

3. Go, silent friend,
   forgive us if we grieved you;
   safe now in heaven,
   kindly say our name.
   Your life has touched us,
   that is why we mourn you;
   our lives without you
   cannot be the same.

4. Go, silent friend,
   we do not grudge you glory;
   sing, sing with joy
   deep praises to your Lord.
   You, who believed
   that Christ would come back for you,
   now celebrate
   that Jesus keeps his word.

The text was originally written for the funeral of an unassuming saint of God, a former cleaning woman who had risked her life during the Nazi occupation of Amsterdam by looking after a Jewish fugitive as if she were a member of the family. This is a song of farewell, most appropriate towards the end of a funeral service or as the casket leaves the church. The tune PSALM 12 (DONNE SEC-OURS) is a beautiful early reformation melody, possibly showing signs of earlier secular dance use. The alternative is arguably the best known traditional Irish melody.

This song is featured in the CD/Cassette and Octavo collections entitled THE LAST JOURNEY. The individual octavo arrangement for soloist, quartet and choir may be found in the GIA catalogue, No.: G4537

76
He is not here

Tune: COISRIGEADH Scots trad. (arr. JLB)

positively ♩ = 55

1. 'He is not here,' the an-gel said to those who searched a-mong the dead. As
2. He is not here. He had to rise a-bove all earth-ly roots and ties, to
3. He is not here. He must pre-pare a place to live, a feast to share for
4. And those who fol-low, Christ will bring where saints con-verse and an-gels sing, where
5. *She* is not here — we dare to claim that one we loved and called by name has
6. And though we can-not know *her* bliss, or feel *her* touch, or take *her* kiss, we

al - ways, Je - sus went be - fore, through
breathe, with un - af - fect - ed breath, be -
all who take him at his word, and
wea - ry bod - ies are made whole and
now been led by God a - bove through
leave *her*, Lord, in your em - brace till

life the Way, through death the Door.
yond the pains of life and death.
put their faith in Christ as Lord.
noth - ing vex - es mind or soul.
death to life, through loss to love.
heaven u - nites us, face to face.

78

1. 'He is not here,' the angel said
   to those who searched among the dead.
   As always, Jesus went before,
   through life the Way, through death the Door.

2. He is not here. He had to rise
   above all earthly roots and ties,
   to breathe, with unaffected breath,
   beyond the pains of life and death.

3. He is not here. He must prepare
   a place to live, a feast to share
   for all who take him at his word,
   and put their faith in Christ as Lord.

4. And those who follow, Christ will bring
   where saints converse and angels sing,
   where weary bodies are made whole
   and nothing vexes mind or soul.

5. *She* is not here— we dare to claim
   that one we loved and called by name
   has now been led by God above
   through death to life, through loss to love.

6. And though we cannot know *her* bliss,
   or feel *her* touch, or take *her* kiss,
   we leave *her,* Lord, in your embrace
   till heaven unites us, face to face.

This song, also for the conclusion of a funeral rite, links the death and resurrection of Christ with that of his disciples. Please note that, depending on the circumstances, 'she' and 'her' in verses 5 & 6 can be changed to he/his/him or they/their/them. An alternative tune in Long Metre is WIN-CHESTER NEW.

80

For all the saints

Tune: O WALY WALY English trad. (arr. JLB)

moderato ♩ = 70

1. For all the saints who showed your
2. For all the saints who loved your
3. For all the saints who named your
4. Bless all whose will or name or

love in how they live and where they
name, whose faith in - creased the Sav - iour's
will, and saw your king - dom com - ing
love re - flects the grace of heaven a -

81

82

1. For all the saints who showed your love
   in how they lived and where they moved,
   for mindful women, caring men,
   accept our gratitude again.

2. For all the saints who loved your name,
   whose faith increased the Saviour's fame,
   who sang your songs and shared your word,
   accept our gratitude, good Lord.

3. For all the saints who named your will,
   and saw your kingdom coming still
   through selfless protest, prayer and praise,
   accept the gratitude we raise.

4. Bless all whose will or name or love
   reflects the grace of heaven above.
   Though unacclaimed by earthly powers,
   your life through theirs has hallowed ours.

This is a simple song of gratitude which may be appropriate, depending on the circumstances, at funeral or memorial services, or around All Saints Day.

This song is featured on the CD/Cassette and Octavo Collections entitled THE LAST JOURNEY. The individual octavo arrangement for choir, oboe and keyboard may be found in the GIA catalogue, No.: G4540

84 Stay with us now

Tune: DARKNESS (JLB)

steadily ♩ = 60

JE - SUS CHRIST, LORD OF ALL,

Find your way a - mong us.

STAY WITH US NOW.

Antiphon: *JESUS CHRIST, LORD OF ALL,*
STAY WITH US NOW.

Verse   1. Find your way among us.

2. Listen to the anxious.

3. Sit beside the lonely.

4. Comfort the despairing.

5. Out of love and mercy,...

6. Do not ever leave us.

7. Even when we doubt you,...

8. Maker of tomorrow,...

(other verses ad lib)

This simple call and response song is flexible in its use, and allows for improvised petitions, depending on the circumstances.

SONGS
FOR
SPECIAL CIRCUMSTANCES

88

A cradling song

Tune: JENNIFER (JLB)

very tenderly ♩ = 70

1. We can-not care for you the way we want-ed, or
2. We can-not watch you grow-ing in-to child-hood and
3. We can-not know the pain or the po-ten-tial which
4. So through the mess of an-ger, grief and tired-ness, through
5. Lord, in your arms which cra-dle all cre-a-tion we

cra-dle you or lis-ten for your cry; but,
find a new u-nique-ness eve-ry day; but
pass-ing years would sum-mon or re-veal; but
ten-sions which are not yet rec-on-ciled, we
rest and place our ba-by be-yond death, be-

89

sep - a - ra - ted as we are by si - lence,
spe - cial as you would have been a - mong us,
for that true ful - fil - ment Je - sus prom - ised
give to God the wor - ship of our sor - row
liev - ing that *she* now, a - live in heav - en,

1.- 4. | 5.

love will not die.
you still will stay.
we hope and feel.
and our dear child.

breathes with your breath.

1.- 4. | 5.

90

1. We cannot care for you the way we wanted,
   or cradle you or listen for your cry;
   but, separated as we are by silence,
   love will not die.

2. We cannot watch you grow into childhood
   and find a new uniqueness every day;
   but special as you would have been among us,
   you still will stay.

3. We cannot know the pain or the potential
   which passing years would summon or reveal;
   but for that true fulfilment Jesus promised
   we hope and feel.

4. So through the mess of anger, grief and tiredness,
   through tensions which are not yet reconciled,
   we give to God the worship of our sorrow
   and our dear child.

5. Lord, in your arms which cradle all creation
   we rest and place our baby beyond death,
   believing that *she* now, alive in heaven,
   breathes with your breath.

The death of a child in the womb during pregnancy, or the birth of a stillborn child, or the gradual fading from life of a tiny baby brings feelings of anger, desolation and deep disappointment which have no parallel in the grief over a friend whose life has run its full course. It is unlikely that any community of people would wish to sing this song. It is best sung by a soloist, though the words—if printed—may be of comfort to those most affected.

92

There is a place

Tune: DUNBLANE PRIMARY (JLB)

very gently ♩ = 60

1. There is a place pre - pared for lit - tle
2. There is a place where hands which held ours
3. There is a place where all the lost po -
4. There is a place where God will hear our
5. Je - sus, who bids us be like lit - tle

chil - dren, those we once lived for,
tight - ly now are re - leased be -
ten - tial yields its full prom - ise,
ques - tions, suf - fer our an - ger,
chil - dren, shields those our arms are

93

94

laugh - ter cruel - ly were torn.
sor - row, tear af - ter tear.
free - ly as they were meant.
lov - ing and of be - lief.
nit - ed; there is a place.

Coda

Great   Choir

Swell

Pedal

molto rall.

1. There is a place prepared for little children,
   those we once lived for, those we deeply mourn;
   those who from play, from learning and from laughter
   cruelly were torn.

2. There is a place where hands which held ours tightly
   now are released beyond all hurt and fear,
   healed by that love which also feels our sorrow,
   tear after tear.

3. There is a place where all the lost potential
   yields its full promise, finds its true intent;
   silenced no more, young voices echo freely
   as they were meant.

4. There is a place where God will hear our questions,
   suffer our anger, share our speechless grief,
   gently repair the innocence of loving
   and of belief.

5. Jesus, who bids us be like little children,
   shields those our arms are yearning to embrace.
   God will ensure that all are reunited;
   there is a place.

This song was written in memory of the sixteen primary school children and their teacher who were killed by a gunman at 9:30 a.m. on Wednesday 13th March 1996, in Dunblane, Scotland. It was never intended as a congregational hymn, though it may be used as such. Its original choral setting allows for reflection on the text which is not possible if everyone is involved in singing.

This song is featured in the CD/Cassette and Octavo collections entitled THE LAST JOURNEY. The individual octavo arrangement for choir and organ is available in the GIA catalogue. No.: G4542

96 What shall we pray?

Tune: KINGSTON (JLB)
Text: (Carnwadric Parish Church Worship Group and JLB)

gently ♩ = 70

1. What shall we pray for those who died,
2. What shall we pray for those who mourn
3. What shall we pray for those who live
4. What shall we pray for those who know
5. What shall we pray for those who fear
6. God give us peace and, more than this,

those on whose death our lives re - lied?
friend - ships and love, their fruit un - born?
tied to the past they can't for - give,
noth - ing of war, and can - not show
war, in some guise, may re - ap - pear
show us the path where jus - tice is;

Si - lenced by war but not de - nied,
Though years have passed, hearts still are torn;
haunt - ed by ter - rors they re - live?
grief or re - gret for friend or foe?
look - ing at - trac - tive and sin - cere?
and let us nev - er be re - miss

1.- 5
6.

God give them peace.
God give them peace.
God give them peace.
God give them peace.
God give them peace.
work - ing for peace that lasts.

1. What shall we pray for those who died,
   those on whose death our lives relied?
   Silenced by war but not denied,
   God give them peace.

2. What shall we pray for those who mourn
   friendships and love, their fruit unborn?
   Though years have past, hearts still are torn;
   God give them peace.

3. What shall we pray for those who live
   tied to the past they can't forgive,
   haunted by terrors they relive?
   God give them peace.

4. What shall we pray for those who know
   nothing of war, and cannot show
   grief or regret for friend or foe?
   God give them peace.

5. What shall we pray for those who fear
   war, in some guise, may reappear
   looking attractive and sincere?
   God give them peace.

6. God give us peace and, more than this,
   show us the path where justice is;
   and let us never be remiss
   working for peace that lasts.

In Scotland, Remembrance Sunday, when the nation honours those who have died in war, can be a fraught occasion. It brings back unspeakably painful memories to some, offends others, and puzzles younger people who have only seen pictures of war. In this song, representatives of a local congregation identified the different people who would be reacting to services of remembrance, holding them together before God with the same prayer.

100 As if you were not there

Tune: ILICH (JLB)

solemnly ♩ = 60

1. As if you were not there, the skies ig - nite and
2. As if you were not there, fa - mine and flood to -
3. As if you were not there, we tel - e - vise the
4. As if you were not there, your Son, when faith de -
5. Be - cause he rose a - gain and showed God's love is

thun - der, ri - vers tear their banks a -
geth - er ush - er death, dis - ease and
dy - ing, watch the help - less vic - tims
fied him, faced a crowd which cru - ci -
vast - er than the ul - ti - mate dis -

1. As if you were not there,
   the skies ignite and thunder,
   rivers tear their banks asunder,
   thieves and nature storm and plunder:
   all beware
   as if you were not there.

102

2. As if you were not there,
   famine and flood together
   usher death, disease and terror;
   stricken mothers wonder whether
   God heeds prayer,
   as if you were not there.

3. As if you were not there,
   we televise the dying,
   watch the helpless victims crying,
   salve our consciences by sighing,
   'Life's unfair!'
   as if you were not there.

4. As if you were not there,
   your Son, when faith defied him,
   faced a crowd which crucified him,
   leaving friends who had denied him
   in despair,
   as if you were not there.

5. Because he rose again
   and showed God's love is vaster
   than the ultimate disaster,
   we entreat you now to master
   strife and pain,
   because he rose again.

Though most of this collection deals with grieving for people known to us, the Church, if it is the Body of Christ, has to share the pain of those we do not necessarily see, but who are bound to us in Christ. So this song and the following one offer lament and prayer for people and places in the world beyond our shores. What is euphemistically called 'natural disaster' lies behind the text of this song.

104 Listen, Lord

Tune: LISTEN, LORD (JLB)

firmly ♩ = 60

LIS - TEN, LORD. LIS - TEN, LORD, NOT TO OUR WORDS BUT TO OUR PRAYER. YOU A - LONE, YOU A - LONE, UN - DER - STAND AND CARE.

Fine

1. Where the voice that once was wel - come
2. Where the wis - dom meant to heal is
3. Where the with - ered hands and hopes stretch
4. Turn the world and spurn the spite of

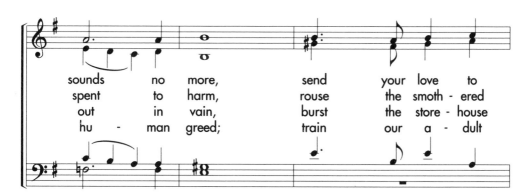

sounds no more, send your love to
spent to harm, rouse the smoth - ered
out in vain, burst the store - house
hu - man greed; train our a - dult

D.C.

homes turned s - ilent, hearts turned sore.
con - science, sound high heaven's a - larm.
of your grace and of our grain.
eyes on where a child may lead.

106 *Chorus:* *LISTEN, LORD. LISTEN, LORD,*
NOT TO OUR WORDS BUT TO OUR PRAYER.
YOU ALONE, YOU ALONE,
UNDERSTAND AND CARE.

1. Where the voice that once was welcome sounds no more,
   send your love to homes turned silent, hearts turned sore.

2. Where the wisdom meant to heal is spent to harm,
   rouse the smothered conscience, sound high heaven's alarm.

3. Where the withered hands and hopes stretch out in vain,
   burst the storehouse of your grace and of our grain.

4. Turn the world and spurn the spite of human greed;
   train our adult eyes on where a child may lead.

If the previous song dealt with the consequences of natural disasters, then this text deals with the grim reality that death in developing countries through war, malnutrition and disease can also be related to the economic or cultural imperialism, the need for arms sales and the overconsumption of raw materials and food which is a feature of life in the 'civilized' West. It is best that this song be sung

Alphabetical index of first lines

108 Associated publications

Many of the songs in this book have been recorded by The Cathedral Singers of Chicago and appear in the CD/Cassette entitled THE LAST JOURNEY. As well as the original texts and tunes printed here, THE LAST JOURNEY recording with its associated OCTAVO pack of the same name, includes settings of spirituals from the USA and AFRICA, as well as through-composed anthems based on scriptural and liturgical texts associated with the ceremonies surrounding death.

A further two items 'A Touching Place' and 'Be Still and Know' have also been recorded by the Cathedral Singers and are represented in Octavos in the GOD NEVER SLEEPS collection

Further hymns, songs, and liturgical materials produced by John L. Bell and Graham Maule may be found in these books, published in Great Britain by Wild Goose Publications (The Iona Community), in North America by GIA Publications, Inc. of Chicago, and represented in Australia and New Zealand by Willow Publications of Sydney.

The Iona Community

The Iona Community is an ecumenical Christian community, founded in 1938 by the late Lord MacLeod of Fuinary (the Rev. George MacLeod DD) and committed to seeking new ways of living the Gospel in today's world. Gathered around the rebuilding of the ancient monastic buildings of Iona Abbey, but with its original inspiration in the poorest areas of Glasgow during the Depression, the Community has sought ever since the 'rebuilding of the common life', bringing together work and worship, prayer and politics, the sacred and the secular in ways that reflect its strongly incarnational theology.

The Community today is a movement of some 200 Members, over 1,400 Associate Members and about 1,600 Friends. The Members — women and men from many backgrounds and denominations, most in Britain, but some overseas — are committed to a rule of daily prayer and Bible reading, sharing and accounting for their use of time and money, regular meeting and action for justice and peace.

The Iona Community maintains three centres on Iona and Mull: Iona Abbey and the MacLeod Centre on Iona, and Camas Adventure Camp on the Ross of Mull. Its base is in Community House, Glasgow, where it also supports work with young people, the Wild Goose Resource and Worship Groups, a bimonthly magazine (*Coracle*) and a publishing house (Wild Goose Publications).

For further information on the Iona Community please contact:

The Iona Community,
Pearce Institute,
840 Govan Road,
Glasgow
G51 3UU

T. 0141 445 4561; F. 0141 445 4295
e-mail: ionacomm@gla.iona.org.uk

Other Titles from WGP

SONGBOOKS with full music (titles marked * have companion cassettes)
THE LAST JOURNEY - PACK OF 15 OCTAVOS* John Bell
THE LAST JOURNEY reflections*, John Bell
THE COURAGE TO SAY NO: 23 SONGS FOR EASTER & LENT*John Bell and
   Graham Maule
GOD NEVER SLEEPS – PACK OF 12 OCTAVOS* John Bell
COME ALL YOU PEOPLE, Shorter Songs for Worship* John Bell
PSALMS OF PATIENCE, PROTEST AND PRAISE* John Bell
HEAVEN SHALL NOT WAIT (Wild Goose Songs Vol.1)* J Bell & Graham Maule
ENEMY OF APATHY (Wild Goose Songs Vol.2) J Bell & Graham Maule
LOVE FROM BELOW (Wild Goose Songs Vol.3)* John Bell & Graham Maule
INNKEEPERS & LIGHT SLEEPERS* (for Christmas) John Bell
MANY & GREAT (Songs of the World Church Vol.1)* John Bell (ed./arr.)
SENT BY THE LORD (Songs of the World Church Vol.2)* John Bell (ed./arr.)
FREEDOM IS COMING* Anders Nyberg (ed.)
PRAISING A MYSTERY, Brian Wren
BRING MANY NAMES, Brian Wren

CASSETTES & CDs (titles marked † have companion songbooks)
CD, THE LAST JOURNEY, † John Bell (guest conductor)
Tape, THE LAST JOURNEY, † John Bell (guest conductor)
Tape, IONA ABBEY, WORSHIP FROM EASTER WEEK (ed/arr Steve Butler)
Tape, THE COURAGE TO SAY NO † Wild Goose Worship Group
Tape, GOD NEVER SLEEPS † John Bell (guest conductor)
CD, GOD NEVER SLEEPS † John Bell (guest conductor)
Tape, COME ALL YOU PEOPLE † Wild Goose Worship Group
CD, PSALMS OF PATIENCE, PROTEST AND PRAISE † Wild Goose Worship Group
Tape, PSALMS OF PATIENCE, PROTEST AND PRAISE † WGWG
Tape, HEAVEN SHALL NOT WAIT † Wild Goose Worship Group
Tape, LOVE FROM BELOW † Wild Goose Worship Group
Tape, INNKEEPERS & LIGHT SLEEPERS † (for Christmas) WGWG
Tape, MANY & GREAT † Wild Goose Worship Group
Tape, SENT BY THE LORD † Wild Goose Worship Group
Tape, FREEDOM IS COMING † Fjedur
Tape, TOUCHING PLACE, A, Wild Goose Worship Group
Tape, CLOTH FOR THE CRADLE, Wild Goose Worship Group

DRAMA BOOKS
EH JESUS...YES PETER No. 1, John Bell and Graham Maule
EH JESUS...YES PETER No. 2, John Bell and Graham Maule
EH JESUS...YES PETER No. 3, John Bell and Graham Maule

PRAYER/WORSHIP BOOKS
THE PILGRIMS' MANUAL, Christopher Irvine
THE PATTERN OF OUR DAYS, Kathy Galloway (ed.)
PRAYERS AND IDEAS FOR HEALING SERVICES, Ian Cowie
HE WAS IN THE WORLD: Meditations for Public Worship, John Bell
EACH DAY AND EACH NIGHT: Prayers from Iona in the Celtic Tradition, Philip Newell

IONA COMMUNITY WORSHIP BOOK,
THE WHOLE EARTH SHALL CRY GLORY, George MacLeod

OTHER BOOKS
COLUMBA: Pilgrim and Penitent, Ian Bradley
THE EARTH UNDER THREAT: A Christian Perspective, Ghillean Prance
THE MYTH OF PROGRESS, Yvonne Burgess
WHAT IS THE IONA COMMUNITY?
PUSHING THE BOAT OUT: New Poetry, Kathy Galloway (ed.)
EXILE IN ISRAEL: A Personal Journey with the Palestinians, Runa Mackay
FALLEN TO MEDIOCRITY: CALLED TO EXCELLENCE, Erik Cramb
REINVENTING THEOLOGY AS THE PEOPLE'S WORK, Ian Fraser

WILD GOOSE ISSUES/REFLECTIONS
A VERY BRITISH MONSTER: A Challenge to UK Immigration Policy, Stanley Hope
A FAREWELL TO THE ARMS TRADE, Bernadette Meaden
A CELEBRATION OF SAINTS: Augustine, Columba and Ninian, Ian Fraser
COMPASSION IN THE MARKETPLACE, Joy Mead
SURPLUS BAGGAGE: The Apostles' Creed, Ralph Smith
THE APOSTLES' CREED: A Month of Meditations, David Levison
WOMEN TOGETHER, Ena Wyatt & Rowsan Malik